THE RAMAYANA

THE RAMAYANA

for young readers

Retold and illustrated
by
Milly Acharya

HarperCollins *Publishers* India

HarperCollins *Publishers* India Pvt Ltd
7/16 Ansari Road, Daryaganj, New Delhi 110 002

First published in 1998 by
HarperCollins *Publishers* India
Fourth impression 2001

Milly Acharya asserts the moral right to be identified
as the author of this version of
The Ramayana, retold and illustrated by her.

ISBN 81-7223-306-X

The Ramayana is designed and typeset by
Arrt Creations
45 Nehru Apartments, Kalkajee
New Delhi 110 019

Typeset in Arrus Bt & Aunt Judy

Printed in India by
Gopsons Papers Ltd
A-14 Sector 60
Noida 201 301

In memoriam
Divakar and Kheya Acharya
A humble tribute from a
prodigal daughter

यन्मातापितरौ वृत्तं तनये कुरुतः सदा।
न सुप्रतिकरं तत्तु मात्रा पित्रा च यत्कृतम्॥

Ayodhyākāṇḍa
Sarga 111, 9

Contents

Chapter 1

On the banks of the sacred river Sarayu stood the ancient city of Ayodhya. It was the capital of King Dashratha's kingdom. Anyone who had travelled to Ayodhya thought that it was a splendid place — its streets were wide and lined with trees and its artisans were skilled and made lovely goods. Nobles and the common people were entertained by dancers and musicians, bringing pleasure to all. And learned scholars shared their wisdom with those who wished to study.

The King was kind and generous to his people. He looked after their welfare and always kept his word. So his subjects respected their wise monarch and upheld the laws of the kingdom. Since the fertile lands were blessed with bountiful harvests, no one ever went hungry. The people lived in harmony and prospered in all they did.

Despite his success and popularity, the old King was unhappy. He had no son to succeed him. Imagine his delight when his prayers were finally answered! His royal heart overflowed with joy when his three queens presented him with four sons. Ram the first, was born to Kaushalya, the eldest queen; the twins, Laxman and Shatrugan were Sumitra's sons; and Kaikeyi, the King's most beloved, named her son Bharat. And of these four, Ram, the eldest, was his father's favourite. The princes grew up together in the royal household, sharing their play and learning their duties. They were not just brothers, they were also the best of friends. And each felt the love of three mothers.

Under the wisest teachers in the kingdom the brothers learned many princely arts and skills. Soon they mastered riding, archery, swordplay, combat rules as well as the graces and manners befitting young princes. They were truthful, honest and devout, and they always respected their elders' wishes. All who saw them admired their fine looks, their knowledge and courage. They also loved the princes dearly for the goodness of their hearts and the sweetness of their nature.

When the princes grew up to be young men, the famous sage Vishwamitra visited the court of Ayodhya. King Dashratha rose from his throne and hastened to greet him.

"Welcome, O holy one! Our city is honoured by your presence. Pray tell me what brings you here and I will do anything in my power to serve you."

"I am preparing a sacred ceremony at my forest hermitage," the visitor replied. "But two clever demons always ruin my efforts — they scatter my offerings and upset the altar. They are sent by Ravana, their king, to torment us. With my expert knowledge of warfare I could easily crush them, but I once vowed never to act in anger. And so I have come to ask you for help. If only you would send your son Ram with me to protect this rite, O King, all would be well."

But the King exclaimed, "Ram? He is a child — barely sixteen-years old! How can he possibly fight against demons? Besides, I couldn't bear to be separated from him. O holy one, I shall send my bravest warriors, my entire army with you. I shall go with you, if necessary, to fight the demons."

The King's reply displeased Vishwamitra. "How unworthy of a noble king!" cried the holy man. "You promised to grant whatever I ask, but now you go back on

your word. Shall I then return to the forest without your help?" King Dashratha dared not offend the royal sage, but neither could he bear to part from his beloved son. What was he to do?

The King's most trusted counsellor knew the princes well, for he was also their teacher. He gently reminded the King, "Ram will come to no harm in Vishwamitra's company. More than this, my Lord, your son will learn many things from the sage's wisdom and knowledge. Besides, O King, it is unwise for a monarch to break his promise and to deny the request of a royal sage."

Dashratha paid heed to these words. It was agreed that Ram would go with Vishwamitra. His inseparable brother Laxman insisted on going with them.

Chapter 2

And so the two princes left the palace on their first journey of adventure. At the outskirts of the city they crossed the river and headed for the forest. It had once been a fertile country, but was now the home to various demons who lurked within the green woodland depths. In a bright clearing at the edge of this forest stood Vishwamitra's hermitage, where he lived with his disciples. Here all was calm and peaceful as the hermits either meditated or were engaged in study.

That very day the sage revealed to the princes an amazing armoury. "For long years I undertook severe trials to please the gods," he explained. "They have rewarded me with these secret weapons." Massive shields and spears, maces, arrows and tridents, missiles and counter-missiles,

all these were his to command. "And of all these magical weapons, the most powerful is the invisible Brahma-astram," he confided, "the ultimate destroyer, which nothing on earth can resist."

So Vishwamitra carefully taught the princes the use of this divine arsenal, and they learned the secret chants which summoned each instrument to their hands. "They are never to be directed at any human being," he instructed. "But against a demon or an enemy of human kind, use them freely."

Vishwamitra began his preparations for the holy rite. Before he took his vow of silence and lit the sacred fire, he reminded the brothers to remain watchful until the sacrifice was completed. They guarded the hermitage from dawn to dusk and from dusk to dawn without a wink of sleep. They watched through to the very last night when the sacred flames blazed more brightly than ever.

Suddenly, in the sky above them, appeared the faces of two fierce demons. The air grew thick with the filth they threw down. Ram and Laxman rose swiftly to defend the sage, absorbed now in his holy ceremony. Ram was the quickest. He hurled a mighty wind missile and blew one demon far out to the ocean, eight hundred miles away. He destroyed the second demon with a flaming discus. Laxman easily scattered the lesser demons into space. The ceremony ended peaceably while Ram and Laxman resumed their watch.

Vishwamitra was very pleased. "Young princes," he said, "thanks to your fearless courage my task is done. I can leave this forest now for the snowy slopes of the Himalayas. On the way to the northern mountains lies the kingdom of Mithila. I must stop there to visit King Janak and I should like you to come with me."

Ram replied, "Honoured teacher, your wish is our command. My brother and I will gladly follow you."

Chapter 3

Now King Janak had a lovely daughter, who was no ordinary child. During a famine, years before, while the King himself was ploughing in a field, he found a small bundle lying along a furrow in the soil. Wrapped within the folds of cloth was an infant girl! His heart was filled with tenderness as he gazed upon her. "She is a precious gift from her mother Earth!" he joyously exclaimed. He took her home to his palace and named her Sita for the furrow wherein she was found. He raised her as his daughter and she became dearer to him than his own life.

King Janak's daughter had by now reached a marriageable age. Noble princes came from distant lands, their hearts on fire with thoughts of love and glory. But the King was determined to choose the best person for his daughter's hand through a test and none had yet succeeded in passing it. The test was this: King Janak possessed a rare and wonderful bow, amazingly heavy and impossible to lift. He had resolved to himself, "Only he who is able to string this bow shall I consider worthy of my precious daughter."

And so, when the three travellers from the forest arrived at Janak's court, the brothers decided to join the crowd of ardent suitors who had gathered to compete once again for Sita's hand. One after the other, noblemen and princes tried to lift the bow, but their efforts were in vain. King Janak glanced at the assembly and inquired, "Is there none among the gallant princes here who is worthy of my daughter's hand?"

Ram stepped forward boldly and replied, "Sir, I will take the challenge upon myself." He was slender and youthful, simply dressed, with the dust from his travels still upon him — a mere lad beside the experienced gallants. Could he possibly succeed where the mighty had failed? Most did not think so.

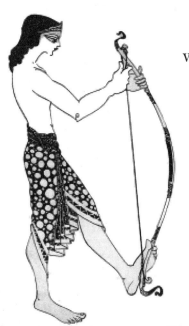

The lords and ladies of the palace watched breathlessly as the slender youth deftly picked up the bow. It yielded easily to his grip. Ram bent the mighty bow effortlessly over his leg to string it. But to the amazement of all, he snapped it into two pieces!

The court rang with cheers. Princes and nobles congratulated him merrily. Sita slowly walked to Ram bearing the bridal garland of fragrant flowers. She placed it around his neck with a smile, pleased to accept him as her husband. King Janak was delighted that of all the many suitors, this young and noble prince had won the contest.

Couriers on swift horses hastened to Ayodhya bearing priceless gifts and joyous news, "Rejoice, O King," they cried through the streets, "for we bring glad tidings and an invitation to a royal wedding!" When he learned their news, King Dashratha's heart swelled with fatherly pride. He gave his consent gladly and set out at once for the ceremony.

King Janak spared no expense for the occasion. His pleasure was boundless when he watched Ram and Sita walk hand in hand around the sacred fire, reciting their marriage vows. The festivities lasted many days and nights, and after much feasting and merry-making, the wedding party prepared to leave Mithila for Ram's royal city of Ayodhya. King Janak showered lavish gifts upon his precious daughter and blessed her lovingly before she left for her new home. He instructed Ram, "Treat my daughter well for she is tender and faithful. I have valued her more dearly than my own life, and now I entrust you with her happiness. May you both prosper!"

In Ayodhya, Ram and Sita were given a hearty welcome. The royal family and their subjects were delighted with this marriage and proud of Ram's achievements. The three queens embraced Sita fondly and led her to her bridal chambers, agreeing amongst themselves, "She is as sweet-natured as she is lovely, and as gentle as she is virtuous." For Sita won their love at once, and she became as a daughter to them.

Chapter 4

For twelve happy years Ram and his brothers helped their father govern the kingdom. When lawless neighbours attacked their boundaries, Ram defended the people. He never lost a single battle. Patiently and kindly he heard the people's grievances, and resolved any dispute brought to him. From the highest to the lowest, his subjects were of one mind: "Ram is always just. No ruler is more noble, no monarch as wise. He is concerned about our welfare and we are devoted to our Prince." His people were safe and at peace with one another.

But one day King Dashratha noticed his reflection in the jewelled walls of the palace and was struck by what he saw. How very old he looked! "I have ruled my kingdom for a long time," he thought to himself. "I know that my people adore Ram, and I can proudly settle the crown upon my son's worthy head. He is wise beyond his years, kind-hearted and honourable. Nothing could please me more than to see my beloved Ram upon the throne of Ayodhya." The King's ministers and his officers heartily approved such an idea. "Let there be no delay," they urged. "Enthrone Ram with all good speed."

Now a coronation is a grand event, and nothing was spared in all the lavish preparations. The streets of Ayodhya were washed and sprinkled with scented water; flower petals were strewn over the path of the procession; the buildings were decorated with pennants and flowers; little earthenware lamps shone brightly along the ceremonial route to light up the night. Carpenters and weavers, masons and builders, jewellers and potters worked with added skill and cheerful energy for the joyous day. Minstrels roamed through every town and village singing sweet songs of Ram's virtues, his noble lineage, of the days of glory to come. People flocked to Ayodhya from the four corners of the kingdom to see the crowning of their beloved prince.

In all the realm could there be even one soul who was not pleased? Ah, but there was! Manthara was the devoted handmaid of Queen Kaikeyi, the favourite wife of the old King. Manthara, now withered and twisted and bent with age, had once rocked the infant princess in her royal cradle, and then followed the young bride to her husband's palace where she served her mistress as loyally as ever. The maid scowled as she watched the joyous preparations.

That very afternoon, as Kaikeyi settled down for her rest, Manthara whispered in her ear, "Once Ram is crowned king, my lady, what do you suppose will happen to you? The power and the glory that you now enjoy, all the favours the old King showers upon you, will vanish entirely. How would you like, instead, to serve Kaushalya, Ram's mother? Can she ever forgive you for winning the King's heart, which once was hers alone? When her son sits upon the throne, she won't let you forget. She will treat you worse than a slave, and there will be no one for you to turn to."

Kaikeyi was horrified at Manthara's words. "What is this you whisper?" she asked. "Ram has always loved and respected his mothers equally. It has never mattered to him that I am not his own mother. And we three queens are such good friends, as close as sisters."

But Manthara was clever. She insisted, "Your own son Bharat is noble and accomplished. He, too, is Dashratha's son, a prince worthy of the crown. If Bharat ruled Ayodhya instead of Ram, think how important you would be. Remember that the Queen Mother holds special place; no one would be above you. My lady, you must act right away or you will lose everything once Ram becomes the king."

Kaikeyi was convinced by Manthara's words and had decided on a plan. She dismissed her maidservant and gave way to angry tears. When her husband came to share his exciting news with her, he was dismayed to find her clothes torn and her eyes glittering with fury. "My precious one!" he exclaimed. "Tell me what grieves you and I promise to return the smile to your face. This I swear upon the life of Ram."

"Do you remember the two wishes you granted me, years ago, when I saved your life on the battlefield?" Kaikeyi asked. The King was a man of his word, and did not make promises lightly. "How could I ever forget? If I am alive today it is only because of you," he answered. "I am delighted that finally, after all these years, there is something you desire."

It was the perfect moment! "I want only two things," Kaikeyi said. "Firstly, it must be my son Bharat, and not Ram, who is crowned king. Furthermore, Ram must be banished from the kingdom for fourteen years."

The King could scarcely believe her words! But no, the Queen was serious. He begged her to demand something else. "I will place all the wealth and jewels in the kingdom at your feet. Order a new palace if you desire. The treasury shall be yours to command. Anything...anything but what you have just asked."

But Kaikeyi held fast. He reasoned with her, "According to our customs it is the eldest son who inherits the kingdom. The crown belongs to Ram. Do you want me to go against our lawful ways?"

"I merely want you to keep your word," Kaikeyi answered. The King could not break a promise, though it broke his heart to summon Ram. He was speechless with sorrow, but Kaikeyi quickly and coldly told the young prince what he must do.

Ram did not despair. He answered very calmly, "My father's honour is more important to me than the crown or the palace. It pleases me to fulfil his promise. I happily leave the kingdom to Bharat. And since you desire it, I shall make for the forest, clad in bark and animal skins, and there lead a hermit's life for the next fourteen years."

The sage Vishwamitra left the court of Ayodhya and headed
towards the forests...

...and the two young princes followed him on their journey of adventure.

Kaikeyi was convinced by the
clever Mantharas words.

NEVER before had Surpanakha seen humans as handsome
as Ram and Laxman.

Chapter 5

So Ram set out with good cheer to seek his mother's blessings and bid farewell to those he loved. The news spread quickly throughout the kingdom. Dismay was on every face. And Sita — how was he ever going to tell her? But Sita would not let Ram leave without her. "I am your wife," she reminded him, "and it is my right to share all your fortunes, whatever they may be. Through good times and through difficult ones I shall stay beside you."

"Life in the forest is much too hard to suit a delicate princess," warned Ram. "When you are hungry or thirsty no one will tend your needs. How will you find shelter from the storms? And where will you rest when you are tired? Wild beasts prowl the forests and danger lurks within its shadows. Why leave the comforts and safety of the palace?

This is the life you were born to, and you must remain a princess."

Sita would not hear of it. She replied, "The forest may be full of hardships but if I am with you I shall enjoy our adventures together. If you leave me here, I shall perish without you." Ram could argue no further, but he was delighted that Sita had won her way.

The loyal Laxman was equally insistent and persuaded Ram to accept his company as well. And so, with painful farewells to parents and crowds of sad well-wishers, Ram, Sita and Laxman left the city of Ayodhya on their long and difficult journey to unknown forests.

King Dashratha could not bear the separation from his favourite son. His heart grew heavy with the burden of his grief. His breath became more faint, his body grew feeble. Soon his life ebbed away. The loss of both Ram and their beloved old king plunged the city of Ayodhya into deep mourning.

Kaikeyi recalled her son, Bharat, from a distant country where the unhappy news had not yet reached him. When he learned of all that had occurred during his absence he was horrified, and angry that his own mother had caused these tragic events. "You aren't my mother, you are my enemy!" he said fiercely. "You banished my dear brothers and killed our beloved father! I have no desire to be king. I shall return the throne to Ram, and in his place I shall spend fourteen years in exile."

Quickly, Bharat assembled a huge procession of townsfolk upon camels, elephants, and horses, and set out to follow Ram's trail into the forest. When, after many weeks of searching they found Ram, Bharat fell at his brother's feet and begged him to return to Ayodhya. But Ram had made up his mind. "We both owe a duty to our father, to honour his word and fulfil the promise he made. It is my own place to live these fourteen years in exile, and it is yours to rule," he said firmly.

Bharat accepted his brother's words. But before he returned to his new kingdom, he insisted on one condition. "I will rule in your name for exactly fourteen years. But you, dear brother. shall still remain the true monarch, even during your absence," Bharat said. "As a reminder to all, I shall place your sandals upon Ayodhya's throne, and there they shall sit beneath the royal canopy until you return. And from this day I too shall live as a hermit in a hut, away from the royal household and its comforts. My spirit will be close to yours through the long years ahead." So with heavy hearts the brothers parted — Bharat in the direction of Ayodhya, and Ram towards the wilderness.

Chapter 6

The three exiles soon forgot the luxuries to which they were born. Now they lived entirely upon the bounty of the forest. They gathered fruits and berries for their food. In place of soft silken couches they slept upon the bare ground and covered themselves with leaves and grass. They built their own shelters, with straight branches for walls and soft rushes for thatch. And they splashed and bathed in nearby streams.

They quickly learned to enjoy their new life and its simple pleasures. "Birds sing so sweetly here and the woodland creatures are so playful," Sita said one day. "The air is always fragrant from the many colourful blossoms. The rippling streams and the cool shade of the trees are refreshing. And the stars — ah, how I love to watch the starry skies at night. I don't miss the comforts of Ayodhya at all!" she laughed. And her two companions agreed with her wholeheartedly.

During their travels a faint shadow was often over them, guarding them from the fiercest rays of the sun or shielding them from sudden bursts of rain. One day the shadow spoke. "I am Jatayu," it introduced itself, "the king of Vultures and a friend of your father, King Dashratha. I promised him that I would always be near at hand to protect or help you in any way I can." And wherever the wanderers went Jatayu was not far behind.

The Vulture-King was not their only friend in the forest. Here, tucked away from the noisy bustle of busy towns, hermits and sages lived in quite seclusion. They were holy men lost in deep meditations, scholars who studied the mysteries of the universe. Their hearts were free from greed and envy, for they wanted nothing and they feared nothing. Their minds were clear, sharp and controlled. Their bodies had grown lean and hard, braving wind and rain and sun. Through the blessings of the gods these sages and hermits came to possess magical powers, secret knowledge, and divine gifts beyond the reach of ordinary mortals. These holy men welcomed the weary wanderers to their humble dwellings, shared food and shelter with Sita and the two princes, and showered blessings upon them.

But the forest was also the lair of demons who threatened the peace of all its inhabitants. They were a menace, for when they prowled the forests no one was safe. And so the peace-loving hermits turned to Ram and Laxman for protection.

One afternoon, while the three companions were hunting in the forest depths, a blood-curdling howl startled them. Over their heads hovered a strange creature. Her eyes glared madly, her hair was a wild tangle of red, and she barked when she spoke. "I am Surpanakha, sister of Ravana, the mighty ruler of Lanka, and King of all demons," growled the wild-eyed demoness from the treetops.

Never before had she seen humans as handsome as Ram and Laxman. In an instant she fell madly in love with them, forgetting her ferocious hunger of a moment ago. "Come with me, you fine little fellows, and we will enjoy one another's company. Won't you frolic with me a while in these forests?" she coaxed.

Ram and Laxman exchanged smiling glances. "My lovely wife is here, so we couldn't possibly keep you company," Ram replied as politely as he could.

"What! That insignificant little mortal? I will swallow her up in one gulp and rid you of her for ever. Then you'll be free as a hawk to marry me," Surpanakha growled. "And what fun we'll have!"

She lunged menacingly at Sita, mouth open and sharp teeth bared, her long claws outstretched. Laxman rushed between them. "Lucky for you that our code forbids noble warriors to kill a woman," he said. And he sliced off her long nose and wrinkled ears with quick, deft strokes of his sword, thus frightening the demoness away. Wailing in agony, she ran into the darkest shadows of the jungle.

"I demand vengeance!" she thundered as she fled swiftly to take refuge in Lanka where the most powerful of her brothers ruled over all

demons. This awful ruler was none other than Ravana, of whom some said even the gods were afraid. But Surpanakha was not afraid to scold even the Demon-King. "What kind of a monarch are you, O brother? How can you allow your fellow demons to be so abused? Two ordinary humans have mutilated your sister and threatened our kinfolk! If you do nothing, you are unfit to be our king!" she said scornfully. "Have you no concern for us, or have your own pleasures made you forget the welfare of your subjects? Act with speed or, I warn you, you will quickly lose all respect in the eyes of others."

Ravana was stung by these taunts. "Your accusations, dear sister, shall not go unanswered. Be assured, Ram and Laxman will perish miserably," he promised. "You have my solemn oath. I shall not rest until I have avenged any harm they have done to our kind, and this shameful insult to you."

Ravana immediately called a council of Lanka's sharpest minds to hatch a clever plot. They reminded him that Ram and Sita were deeply attached to each other. "If by some trick Sita could be brought to Lanka, Ram will surely follow, seeking her out," his advisors proposed. "Once in Lanka, you will easily subdue Ram. Here he would be on alien ground, cut off from the support of his friends and entirely at your mercy." It was a cunning plan, and Ravana chuckled approvingly.

"I shall capture Sita myself, and bring her in bondage to Lanka," he announced with pleasure. The Demon-King boarded his fantastic flying chariot Pushpak, which he had stolen from the gods many years before. It moved through the air with amazing speed and brought him to the doorstep of his friend Maricha.

The two demons disguised themselves — Maricha changed himself into a deer, the most exquisite deer in the world. Ravana dressed in the tattered robes of an ascetic, becoming to all appearances a holy man who wandered alone in the forests, begging for food and living mildly on charity. It was a most dangerous disguise.

Chapter 7

One bright morning while Sita was picking flowers in the garden around her forest shelter, she spied a deer playing nearby. It was no ordinary deer — it was golden! Its colours were luminous one instant, sparkling the next. One moment it seemed shy, the next moment it became quite bold. Sometimes it mingled with the herd, at other times it strayed away on its own. Its dazzling flanks and its charming ways enticed Sita completely.

She called to Ram and Laxman, "Come out and look at this enchanting deer. Wouldn't it make a delightful pet? It will keep me company when you and brother Laxman are away hunting. I would never be lonely again," she pleaded softly with Ram.

When he saw her heart was set on having the deer, Ram found it impossible to refuse. He gently consented to bring the deer to Sita. "Dear brother Laxman," he said, "be sure to protect Sita well while I'm gone. On no condition must you leave her side for even a moment. All is not quite as it appears. Be on your guard, brother."

So Ram set out in quiet pursuit. But the animal wandered deeper and deeper into the forest, farther and farther from their little hut. Its colours shimmered in the light and its grace and golden sheen set it apart from the rest of the herd. Ram followed the deer closely, but it was impossible to catch such a shifty creature! At last, he fitted an arrow to his bow and aimed it at the deer. It went straight to the animal's heart. Instantly the deer changed into Maricha and cried out loudly in Ram's own voice, "Oh Sita! Oh Laxman!" Ram saw through the trick at once. He sensed grave danger, and he promptly turned back to the hermitage.

Maricha's dying cry resounded mournfully through the forest. When Sita and Laxman heard it they were panic-stricken. Sita begged, "Oh Laxman, I beseech you, find out what has happened to Ram. Your brother needs your help. Did you not hear the distress in his voice? Go at once to his aid!"

Laxman hesitated. "It would not be wise, gentle sister, to leave you unattended. I suspect foul play," he replied. But Sita would not listen to reason. She urged and pleaded with her brother. Reluctantly Laxman agreed. Before leaving her he swiftly drew a circle around the hut with the tip of an arrow. "If you do not cross this line, no harm can befall you," he warned her. "No matter what happens, remain within this magic circle, dear sister, until my brother and I return. Only within the circle will you be safe."

No sooner was Sita alone in the hermitage than a feeble ascetic came by, begging for food and alms. "Gracious lady, have mercy on a poor starving creature," he pleaded. "I have roamed the forest for days on end with neither food nor drink. Surely you can spare a little something for a harmless beggar?"

While Sita served him kindly, the stranger watched her every move: her clothes were coarse, her hair was matted, her feet were bare, but she had a pleasing form and gracious manner. And he was charmed. In a faint voice he asked, "Dear lady, I can barely reach the cup you have so kindly offered. Pray, bring it closer so I may drink." Sita hesitated for a moment, remembering Laxman's parting caution. But her heart filled with pity at

the old man's plight, and she thought, "What harm can this miserable stranger do? He scarcely has the strength to raise the cup to his lips. I must help him."

As she stepped out of the ring that Laxman had drawn, she asked, "Pray, sir, who may you be and why do you wander alone in the forest?"

In an instant muscular arms grasped her firmly! Sita had stepped over the line and could not return to the circle of safety. Then Ravana, the King of demons, revealed his real self. "I am here to take you away to my faraway Lanka, O bounteous lady!"

Sita was terrified at the sudden change from a humble beggar into this mighty monster! She could not struggle. "O Demon-King, your evil plan can never succeed," she cried. "When Ram finds out about this, his wrath will bring untold misery upon you and all the demons of Lanka. Believe me, he will leave no stone unturned until he finds me and punishes you."

Ravana roared with laughter and boasted, "What can Ram do when even the gods are afraid of me? If Ram truly cared for you, my lady, would you live in such hardship, following him barefoot through this wilderness, at the mercy of wild beasts and prowlers? Forget Ram, charming one; give yourself to me. Marry me and you shall be my chief queen. All the pleasures of glorious Lanka shall be yours for the asking."

Sita's anger made her bolder. She refused scornfully. "Wretch!" she cried. "My heart belongs to Ram. He is as mighty as the gods, and his anger is as dreadful. If you do anything to offend me, you will regret it."

Her warning fell on deaf ears. Ravana swelled to a demon of towering height, with ten heads and twenty arms. As he picked up Sita and carried her to the magical Pushpak a shadow descended upon him and a pointed beak and sharp talons struck at the Demon-King. The Vulture-King had seen all and had flown to Sita's defence. But Ravana was quicker yet. He took out his sword and with two swift strokes he cut off the bird's wings and left it bleeding while Sita begged mercy for her friend.

Heedless of her pleas the Demon-King mounted the Pushpak and at his command, it rose above the treetops and turned south to Lanka. Far below, Sita saw fleetingly the familiar trees and forests, glades with silvery streams, the animals and birds she loved so fondly. "My good friends, tell Ram I am being taken away by Ravana against my will," she cried out.

Ravana was thrilled with his success. "Ram values nothing more highly than Sita, and I have captured her," he thought with demonic satisfaction. "If I can win her heart, if she chooses me over her lawful husband, then Ram will be thoroughly disgraced. The conquest of his wife will be a glorious triumph for me and a grand insult to Ram!"

But Sita would consent to nothing the Demon-King proposed, and he was furious with her. "Lovely as you are," he threatened fiercely, "I shall not hesitate to have you cooked and served upon my table. You have one year to change your mind. One way or other, you will belong to me. Come to me willingly, or you will come to my tables as a tasty morsel upon a golden platter." And off flew the magical Pushpak to the golden island of Lanka with the terrible Ravana and his lovely captive.

Though she was his prisoner, Ravana treated Sita with the special care befitting a royal princess. He desired her for his wife, and resolved to win her at any cost. "If gracious manners please her, why, I can be gallant and courtly for a year," he thought. "I shall amaze her with my wide knowledge and fabulous wealth. I shall pamper her daily. Before long she will gladly accept me, for who can resist my charms?"

He knew that Sita enjoyed flowers and birds and trees, so he gave her the most delightful pleasure garden in all of Lanka. Peacocks danced for her amidst the trees, like bursts of blue fire, fanning their jewelled tails; brilliant butterflies flitted in playful sparkles from flower to flower. Spotted deer came at her call and nuzzled against her gently, tame and trusting. Birds sang morning and evening in strange, sweet notes, and the scent of orchids floated through the soft air.

One morning while Sita picked
flowers in the garden she spied
a deer playing nearby.

As soon as Sita was
alone in the hermitage
Ravana, dressed as a
feeble
ascetic, came begging for
food and alms.

Ravana turned his blazing eyes upon the monkey
who had dared to disturb Lanka.

"The Ashoka grove is your home, O lovely Sita, until you change your mind," Ravana growled. But it was also her prison; she could never escape the watchful eyes of the demonesses who guarded her, whether she was awake or asleep.

Chapter 8

Far away in the forest where Sita had been captured moments before, Ram and Laxman came upon each other. They knew at once that some terrible calamity had befallen her. They hastened back to their hut. There was no trace of Sita! "I should never have left her, O brother," Laxman lamented. "Who can tell what fearful misfortune may have struck her?"

They looked near and far, they called her name, they searched her favourite spots. Empty silence was all they heard. No bird sang, no woodland creatures played among the leaves, no breeze sighed. Ram was beside himself, but he would not stop his frantic search. And then the brothers heard the feeble moans of the dying Vulture-King, their father's faithful friend. "Demon tricks!" he gasped with his last breath, and that was the only clue he could offer.

Help was near at hand, for deep in the forest where they searched for Sita was a high hill, the home of an enormous band of forest-folk. They were furry little creatures with strong limbs and long, supple tails. Nimble and swift, they could scamper to great heights and travel long distances through the trees. They were called 'The Monkey People' by those who knew them. Like all monkeys, they loved to play and tease and do their clever mischief.

Now when these monkey-folk spied Ram and Laxman approaching their stronghold, their messenger Hanuman came out with a hearty welcome. The brothers quickly told him their sad tale. Hanuman brought them up to his lord Sugriva and begged the brothers to repeat their story. The Monkey-King was not alarmed when he heard their distress; he only smiled and said, "We are strong, we are quick, and we are very clever. We will find your Sita and bring her back to you."

In a flash, millions of the little forest-folk clambered onto the treetops and set out in every direction. "Whoever is first to spy Sita and bring me word will receive rich rewards and honours befitting a hero," Sugriva called after them. If anyone was likely to discover Sita, Ram felt it would be Hanuman. So he took the signet ring off his finger and told Hanuman that Sita would immediately trust the messenger who showed her that ring.

Now, a sharp-eyed bird who could see beyond the vast forests, through the highest mountain and across the widest ocean, had already spied Sita in her far-away garden. He flew quietly to Hanuman, and perched above him in a tree. "I see Sita in a most beautiful grove, surrounded by tall trees, amidst tinkling fountains," whispered the great bird. "The garden lies on the island of Lanka."

The mystery was solved! Lanka was the domain of the fearful Ravana; he was the culprit who had abducted Sita. A wide stretch of blue ocean lay between his kingdom and the land of Ram and Laxman. How would they get there? Hanuman was the most courageous and swiftest of all the monkey-folk; he volunteered to leap across the sea onto that distant island in quest of Sita.

First, he looked up at the heavens and prayed for blessings. Next, he planted his feet firmly on the ground and stretched his tail upon his back. Then, with a deep breath and a mighty roar, he leaped high, high, and away, sailing through the air over the deep blue sea to the firm, sandy beaches of Lanka.

Hanuman landed lightly on the shore. He wished neither to be discovered by the islanders, nor to frighten Sita, so he drew in his mighty breath and he quickly shrank to the size of a little kitten. Now he could climb trees and scale walls without being noticed by the terrible townsfolk on Ravana's island kingdom.

The city stood atop a three-peaked mountain, ringed by high walls and encircled by a deep moat. Upon its battlements sentries kept watch day and night. Four enormous gates led into the city and no strangers were allowed entrance. Armed guards stood at every corner. "My friends and I must soon face this dreadful enemy!" Hanuman reckoned.

Searching for Sita, he beheld a flourishing city! The buildings were grand, each one surrounded by lovely gardens where fountains splashed amidst brightly coloured flowers. There were crystal palaces with towers that pierced the sky. The doorways of the great mansions were inlaid with gold and gems, dazzling as the sunlight. The townspeople walked tall and straight, richly clad, unaware of the little monkey watching them.

Chapter 9

When at last Hanuman arrived at the Ashoka grove, he spied Sita forlorn amidst her guards. Hanuman approached her quietly as only a kitten could, and in gentle tones he whispered, "I come to you, most gracious lady, as a messenger from Ram. Your husband misses you greatly, and is beside himself with anxiety. He is determined to rescue you from your captor, no matter where you are hidden, no matter who guards you."

Sita heard these words of comfort with great relief. "For months," she told him, "I have not set eyes on a friendly face, nor heard a kindly voice. How I wish I could reward you, gentle soul, for the joy and consolation you bring me. But alas! I have nothing to give you." She recounted to

Hanuman all the misadventures that had befallen her. "Pray tell my husband how I long to be with him," she implored.

"Most certainly, sweet mistress. I'll hasten away with my news," the trusty messenger promised. "We shall all return in full force to your rescue. It grieves me to leave you now, but Ravana must be taught a lesson. There is no time to lose." Hanuman gave Sita the signet ring from Ram, and her heart was touched with longing for her husband. She pulled a jewelled ornament from her hair for Hanuman to take back for Ram, knowing it would prove to her husband that she was still alive.

Despite his hurry, Hanuman was a true monkey. He could not resist a little mischief-making before he left Lanka. He blew himself back into his enormous size and with all his strength he shook and crushed the grand mansions that stood along his path. "These demons have pestered others for long enough. Now it's their turn for a little surprise," Hanuman chuckled. "I'll give them a nice dose of their own medicine!" He uprooted the trees and knocked down the walls around him; he had a grand time prancing recklessly along.

But word quickly reached Ravana. "A monkey is loose in the streets of Lanka, Your Majesty, and he is causing havoc throughout the city!" his messengers exclaimed. "Go quickly then," Ravana ordered his soldiers, "and bring this trouble-monger to me!"

Bands of demon soldiers poured out of the royal palace and soon the brave monkey was surrounded. Hanuman fought them one by one, but he was finally trapped. The demons bound him hand and foot and brought him before their king. Hanuman was curious for a glimpse of the court anyway, and he thought, "What a rare privilege! Few can boast of an audience with the mighty monarch and live to tell the tale."

Ravana's palace was indeed magnificent. Hanuman was led through towering archways into enormous halls where

patterns of colourful gems glittered upon elegant pillars and across vaulted ceilings. His eyes grew round with awe and he was dazzled by the brilliance of it all. And there, upon his throne beneath a golden canopy, sat Lanka's majestic ruler, surrounded by courtiers and attendants.

"How noble and heroic he seems!" thought Hanuman. "Such fabulous wealth, such grandeur! With all his knowledge and skills, Ravana could have been a splendid ruler. Instead, he torments others for his own pleasure. He is selfish and full of malice. Such talents are wasted on him!"

Ravana turned his blazing eyes upon the monkey who had dared to disturb the blissful Lanka. "Rascal!" he fumed. "A monkey's tail is his pride. I wonder what we can do with yours?" Turning to his slaves, he ordered, "Let his tail be dipped in oil and set on fire. That should be fit punishment for a meddlesome monkey!"

The demon-guards paraded the monkey with his blazing tail through the city streets, but Hanuman had seen enough. He drew in his breath. His bonds burst apart easily and he darted away. He ran about the city gleefully, torching everything along his path and causing even more damage than before. Then, satisfied with his revenge, Hanuman leapt into the air and with a mighty roar he was gone.

Chapter 10

Hanuman's friends on the other side of the ocean were overjoyed to hear news of Sita. Hanuman quietly placed Sita's jewel in Ram's hand. Ram fondly embraced him. "You are a true hero, good friend. My heart feels lighter knowing Sita is alive and unharmed. With your help, O bravest of the brave, we can hasten to her rescue."

In great detail, Hanuman informed the monkey-people of Lanka's military might, of its lofty city walls, its many fortresses and arsenals. "The best strategy," they all agreed, "is to set out immediately for Lanka. Ravana's spies will have less time to discover our plans and to plot against us." So Sugriva quickly summoned the countless monkey-folk. Tribes of every description — pale ones and dark ones, tawny, gold and russet ones, young and old ones — all came running at his call.

They set about eagerly to build a long bridge to Lanka. Together they fetched stones and boulders and brought them to the seashore. Then they piled them in massive heaps across the sea. Five days of hard work, no mischief and no pranks, but much scampering, and the stretch of ocean was bridged. Millions of forest-folk, with Ram, Laxman and Sugriva in the lead, crossed over to the island kingdom where Sita waited in her garden.

Their arrival in Lanka did not remain a secret for too long. Ravana's spies rushed the news to his court. "Crush them!" "Sweep them into the ocean!" "Let us attack them!" his counsellors roared. Ravana's brother, Vibhisan, was the only one who disagreed. "To steal another man's wife is always evil. It is not too late, O brother, to return Sita and cool Ram's anger," he advised. "Her presence here endangers all our lives. Do not let your desires overshadow Lanka's safety."

Ravana would not listen; in fact, it made him more angry. "Enough!" he exclaimed. "You are more concerned for the enemy than for us. Go, join Ram and befriend him. We can do far better without you on our side!" Vibhisan, knowing himself to be right, went over to Ram's side. However, the Demon-King was firm in his evil scheme. "I am certain that when Ram is dead, Sita will seek my love and protection," he thought. And he was ready to plunge into battle in his eagerness to destroy Ram.

Ravana's demons were fierce warriors, massively built, with sturdy armour and deadly weapons. They were confident of winning, for their leader was said to be indestructible. His many brothers and his great sons and nephews were renowned heroes of many bloody battles. "We have nothing to fear from these little pests, whose only weapons are their sharp teeth and long tails," the demons boasted.

Now Ravana summoned his generals. "Prepare to attack!" he thundered. Trumpets roared. Battle-drums beat a furious rhythm. The mighty bronze doors of the fortress swung open and out charged the great war elephants arrayed in brocade and golden tassels. Armoured chariots rushed by, magnificent horses on the gallop, manes flying and breath steaming. The piercing sound of the conch-shell rent the air. With great fanfare the war began in earnest.

Thirsty for blood, the demons thundered down the slopes to the battleground. They charged the little enemy, slashing and hewing in all directions. But the forest-folk stood their ground; they flung rocks and stones at the onrushing hordes. They uprooted trees and hurled them with great force. Blood spurted, limbs were torn, heads and bodies were crushed. Many lives were lost that terrible day, on both sides. The brave forest-folk returned the demons' terrible assault. They sent wave after wave of fearless marauders on the attack.

The demons were baffled and furious! "These puny monkeys have killed our greatest heroes one after another," they reported to their king. "How is it possible?"

Ravana saw his mighty army shrinking, and he knew then that his forces must have a fearsome general to defend Lanka. "There is still my brother to call upon. Go at once," he ordered, "and awaken Kumbhakarna."

Chapter 11

Now Kumbhakarna was so fearsome a demon-warrior that the gods made sure he slept for six months at a time. He would awaken for a single day to prowl the earth and feast his enormous appetite before he yawned and dozed off again for another six months. It required thousands of elephants, trumpeting fearfully, to wake up the slumbering giant!

When this terrible monster learned that his brother needed him for battle he hastily buckled on his armour and collected his weapons. Even in his hurry he felt his mighty hunger gnawing at his stomach and his massive jaws watered at the thought of food. "I cannot wait to gorge myself upon the enemy," he chortled.

Like an avalanche he descended upon the battlefield, grabbing the little forest-folk he passed and swallowing them greedily. The rocks they hurled at him were as dust which he lightly brushed off. Who would blame the poor monkey-folk if, for just a moment, their courage fled at the sight of the huge monster?

Laxman charged to the rescue of his friends, but the giant roared, "Brave as you are, O prince, it is with Ram that I seek to do battle. And when I am done with him then I shall feast upon you both, and as many of your friends as still remain."

The giant lunged at Ram, waving an iron club in one hand and an uprooted tree in the other. But quick as lightning Ram aimed a wind missile at the monster and swept away his muscled arms. Still the demon stormed on, kicking enormous boulders until Ram blew away both his legs. Without limbs he hurtled forward with astounding fury until a crescent blade from Ram's quiver severed his head from his body. It fell to the ground with a heavy thud, and as it rolled along it dislodged rocks and knocked down trees until it reached a standstill on level ground.

The silence that followed sounded ominous to the Demon-King and his courtiers. Ravana's son Indrajit, who had earned his name by once defeating the mighty god Indra, watched the destruction from the great heights of the royal palace. He consoled his angry father, saying, "Do not despair, my Lord, for Lanka is safe as long as I live. Give me leave to crush the enemy and sweep them off our shores." Proud of his terrible son and sure of his powers, Ravana blessed him and sent him to battle.

The clever Indrajit was renowned for his magic. He could make himself invisible! So he ascended his armoured chariot boldly and rose into the air like a feather in the wind. The marvellous chariot hovered over the battlefield, concealed in a cloud of smoke. "Those puny pests will be helpless against a foe they cannot see!" thought the Demon-Prince. He jubilantly rained arrows upon them, arrows which became a torrent of lions' teeth and stinging scorpions' tails as they reached the earth. The shafts from his bow burst into burning sparks that scorched his victims, and thousands fell before his eyes.

The monkey force set about eagerly to build the
long bridge to Lanka.

Hanuman lifted the great mountain upon the palm of his
hand and flew across the ocean again.

Sita slowly entered the crackling flames.

Amidst joyous festivity, Ram was enthroned at last.

Laxman knew that the arrows coming from the cloud could only be Indrajit's. He was heartbroken at the sight of his dear friends in such deadly straits. "We must stop Indrajit at any cost," he warned Hanuman. So together the two comrades lured the Demon-Prince from his chariot amidst the clouds to the bloody field. "You are no match for me, young prince. I could tear you into bits with my bare hands!" Indrajit sneered. "Save your breath, you boastful one. I challenge you to single combat!" Laxman replied.

In the heat of their fury they became a mad whirl of battling figures. Their skills were well-matched, so their struggle seemed endless. At last Laxman, looking to the heavens, prayed fervently, "If Ram is indeed devoted to truth and duty, let Indrajit's defeat prove it!"

Feeling suddenly a new power surge through his arms, he let fly a razor-sharp disc, and Indrajit's handsome young head fell smoking to the ground. The forest-folk cheered in triumph. Leaderless now, and panic-stricken, the demons fled for safety within their city walls. The monkey-warriors threw blazing torches at their retreating backs. The demon-cries reached Ravana's ears, and he knew instantly what those sounds meant! Grieved as he was, this was no time for lamenting.

Chapter 12

When the last of his valiant heroes failed to return, Ravana knew his own turn to confront Ram had finally come. Dressed in his shimmering armour of solid gold, brilliant gems sparkling upon his chest and crown, Ravana mounted his war-chariot. Glossy black horses strained at the reins, ready to charge. His battle-flag fluttered in the wind.

"Be warned!" he thundered, "for today I shall put an end to you all. No longer will you menace the soil of Lanka!" The forest-folk sent showers of rocks and trees at his approach, but these merely rolled off his body. He answered with flaming darts that felled thousands of the monkey-people and drove terror into their hearts.

Laxman rushed to assist his loyal friends. As Ravana saw him he vowed, "You, mortal prince, shall bear the full force of my fury!" An earth-shattering thunderbolt knocked Laxman senseless to the ground. Seeing his dearest brother in a pool of blood and barely alive, Ram lost all heart for battle. The forest-folk gathered round quickly to protect Laxman, while Ravana growled and threatened them. For he was surer now of his conquest than he had been since Lanka was beset with these puny invaders.

The monkeys whispered to Ram, "We know of medicinal herbs which restore life, but these grow only on a mountain-side far away in the snow-capped Himalayas." Who would go such a great distance and return while there was still breath in Laxman's body? Hanuman! For he was fast as the wind and swiftly he flew off to the lofty mountains. Before he knew it, he was standing on a rocky slope among the clouds. But he was bewildered by the number of different plants which grew there. "I am no wise healer," he mused. "If I return with the wrong herbs, I will be unable to help Laxman."

But where Hanuman's wits failed him, his great strength saved Laxman. Wasting no time, the monkey hero lifted the great mountain upon the palm of his hand and carried it to the plain where Laxman lay lifeless. The wise forest-folk

selected the right herbs and
ground them into a potion
while Hanuman returned
the mountain to its
original place. And
no sooner did
Laxman inhale
the vapours of the herbs
than his wounds began to heal.

Now Ram's courage returned.
He sprang from the ground ready to do
final battle, fearless of the monster's
ten heads and countless arms. Both the combatants had
powerful weapons which were blessed with magical
properties. Each was skillful and valiant. And neither one
had ever tasted defeat.

Soon the sky was ablaze once again with heat and
flames from the clash of arms. Tremors shook the earth, the
ocean churned gigantic waves, the heavens darkened
ominously. All living creatures trembled with fear; their
howls echoed through the island forests. Ram and Ravana
fought with all their might while on both sides the other
warriors stood by to watch the awesome combat.

Ravana's weapons released ferocious animals. The heads of lions, crocodiles, vicious serpents and snarling jackals hurled down through the air. But Ram merely froze these beasts into ice which broke into pieces the moment they touched the ground. Ravana aimed tridents filled with deadly venoms, but Ram's poisons were equally potent. The twang of his bow could be heard for miles as he drew the string back to his ear and discharged a storm of arrows straight at his foe.

The demon's eyes blazed, he breathed smoke through his nostrils, his mouth twisted in rage. His twenty arms wielded twenty weapons at once! "I am no mortal," the Demon-King reminded Ram. "The gods in their heavens fear me. Do you dare test my superhuman strength?" Ram cut off Ravana's head in reply. Another head instantly replaced it, and when he cut this one off as well, a new head appeared in its place. The monster was impossible to defeat! Of all the magical arms that Ram posessed, none had any effect on Ravana.

It was then that Ram remembered the one weapon he had never tested. The time had come to use it — the most deadly weapon, the missile which was the gift of Lord Brahma himself. No being on earth could endure its destructive might. It could tear open the skies or dry up the oceans.

Ram repeated the chant that would summon it, and there in his hand it gleamed in the waning sunlight, invisible to all but Ram alone. He blessed it silently, then hurled it with full force at his enemy. With a thundering roar the Brahma–astram exploded into the depths of the earth, crushing the mighty Ravana on its way. The spot was deeply gouged, like a great wound upon the ground, and poisonous fumes rose thick and fast from its dark crater. Neither tree nor grass nor weed would grow here, and for many years the land remained stubbornly barren.

Their leader was dead! With panic in their hearts and fear in their bones, the defeated demons turned and fled, easily routed by the exuberant monkey-army. Very soon the field of battle lay empty and silent. The skies cleared, the sun shone cheerfully, gentle breezes cooled the air, the earth ceased to shudder, and the waves were calm once more.

Ram and his friends were safe; Lanka was quiet and serene. Ravana's brother Vibhisana, who had helped Ram achieve his victory, was now crowned the new ruler of Lanka.

Chapter 13

But poor Sita was still a captive in the Ashoka grove. The terrible din had filled her with anxiety for Ram and Laxman and their devoted friends. She longed to see her husband and learn from his own lips that he was safe.

"It is time to convey the news of our triumph to Sita, and to release her," Ram announced. But was it not strange that he did not carry the news himself? Once more he sent the trusted Hanuman to Sita with his message. She was overjoyed that she could be reunited with her husband. But her first meeting with Ram, when Hanuman brought her before him, was quite different from what she had expected.

Ram did not rush to greet Sita when she came to him. He merely nodded to her from where he stood. Before the entire assembly he informed her, "I have defeated Ravana.

Now you are free. Do as you please. You may stay in Lanka with Vibhisana or join Sugriva if you prefer. Follow Laxman if you like or go to Bharat," he suggested. He seemed reluctant to take her back. But why?

Sita asked him to explain this strange and cold pronouncement. "We have been separated for almost a year," he answered her. "You have been with Ravana and have accepted his hospitality these many months. How can I be certain that you are still as faithful to me as you once were?"

Her husband's words wounded Sita deeply. Ram was asking her before this enormous gathering of strangers to prove that her loyalty was complete and unshaken. How could he doubt her? Janak's daughter felt shamed and insulted.

She turned slowly to Laxman. "Light a fire," she ordered. Then she faced Ram. "These flames will consume me if in heart or thought I was ever disloyal to you. Ravana forcibly carried me to Lanka where, against my will, he held me captive. I did not accept his hospitality. He tried to win my favours, but I have cared for no one but you. If even for an instant I have been untrue, let the fire devour me. But if, as I claim, I have remained faithful, the fire will not harm a single hair of my head."

There was a tense silence while the fire was lit. Logs were piled on flaming logs, and soon the blaze was roaring. Sita seemed fearless as she prepared herself for the test. Before her first step, she looked up to the heavens and begged the gods above to be her witnesses. All eyes were fastened on her as she slowly entered the crackling flames. Suddenly the air was filled with the piercing shrieks of the women in the crowd, for the shimmering orange heat had swallowed Sita. The piteous wailing ceased in amazement when Janak's daughter emerged from the scorching blaze unharmed, radiant and lovelier than ever.

Then all the warriors and all Ram's friends and followers were certain that she had not been dishonoured by Ravana. Only now would Ram embrace Sita. He softened to her. "It was not I who suspected you of disloyalty. But as a ruler," he said loftily, "I am obliged to satisfy my subjects. While I trust your word, they require proof of your purity. They are my subjects, you see. How could they respect their king if he accepted an unfaithful wife? Your test by fire was the perfect way to dispel their suspicions." "That may well be," answered Sita with solemn dignity. "But you will test me again at your own peril."

Chapter 14

The fourteen long years of exile were over and Ram was eager to return to Ayodhya. King Vibhisana offered Pushpak, the celestial craft, to speed their homeward journey. Ram, Laxman and Sita, with all the forest-folk, boarded the vehicle and left the island of Lanka behind them in peace. Very soon they alighted on the outskirts of Ayodhya. Ram once more sent Hanuman with a message, this time for Bharat, announcing their return.

Bharat's joy knew no bounds! He arranged a splendid reception to welcome his victorious brothers and all their friends. Heralds were despatched to spread the triumphant news and throughout the kingdom there was tremendous rejoicing. Once again music and laughter were heard in the streets of Ayodhya.

"My brother's coronation shall be a grand affair! We must prepare for it at once," Bharat declared. The delighted citizens immediately set to work. Streamers were hung across the roads and flags waved gaily in the breeze. Floral wreaths decorated the houses and thousands of oil lamps twinkled like stars upon balconies, windowsills and rooftops. Visitors were offered food and drink, while musicians, dancers and acrobats entertained them. People thronged the streets of Ayodhya, dressed in their finest clothes. The priests, meanwhile, lit the sacred fires and made their offerings to the gods; they called blessings upon the land and began their chants for the long-awaited ceremony.

The city of Ayodhya welcomed the war-weary travellers with open arms and loud cheering. From their windows, upon their balconies, and along the streets citizens shouted, "Victory!" and "Long live Ram!" And the three queens, with tears running down their cheeks, fondly embraced their sons after fourteen lonely years. The brothers were thrilled to be reunited, and they had much to tell one another.

Before the start of the ceremonies, Ram gave Sita a necklace of exquisite pearls. She immediately sought out Hanuman, whose friendly face had brought her hope and comfort during her confinement in Lanka. "I want you to have this as a token of my deepest gratitude and fond affection, O best of friends!" she said, He beamed with pleasure as Sita placed her gift around his neck, and his tail stretched proudly for all to see.

Amidst joyous festivity, with all the blessings of his elders and citizens, Ram was enthroned at last. The gods were honoured with sacrifices and prayers, and they smiled kindly upon the new king and his vast domain. Ram's rule was long and prosperous. The rain came when it was needed to cool the land and nourish the soil. The skies cleared in time to ripen the crops. The seasons were mild, the earth bountiful, the trees bore plenty of fruit, and everyone was content. Under the wise and kind rule of their righteous king people were free from fear, and for several years peace and goodness reigned throughout the land.

Did Ram ever choose to put Sita to the test again? You may well wonder. But therein lies another very long tale.

THE END

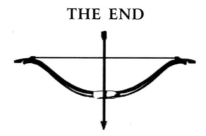